Four 1 ... at the Zoo

(An Adventure with Friends who are Different)

By Angel Tucker, CHBC
and
Robert A. Rohm, Ph.D.

Illustrated by Steve Pileggi

Personality
INSIGHTS
PRESS

Welcome to the "Four Pals"™ Series!

These books were created for three reasons:

1. To show children that they were uniquely created - even our personalities.

2. To teach children all about the different personality types!

3. To let children know that it's okay to feel unique and special as well as be different from their friends!

Here is a further description of each of the personality types. This should assist you in giving your children a better idea of how each of us is different. The important fact to remember is that all children have a unique blend of ALL FOUR of these personality styles. No one will fit neatly into one style. All children will possess some of all of these traits and will exhibit each of the four different types of behavior at different times. Usually, however, one style will emerge as the most predominant trait and this will be the trait the child will demonstrate most often. It will also be the trait that he or she will be most comfortable using on a daily basis. We often say, "That is the way they are wired!"

David

DAVID is our wonderful "D" type personality! The letter "D" represents the word "**Dominant**." "D" type personalities love to be in charge and have things done their own way. "D"s think fast and move fast! Their communication style is bottom line oriented. Their attitude is lead, follow, or get out of my way! You never have to wonder what a "D" is thinking – they will just tell you! "D" children are usually the ones leading all the group activities and telling all the other kids what they will be doing. The "D" type personality is **Outgoing and Task-oriented**!

For more great tips on understanding the D-I-S-C child, please get a copy of *A+ Ideas for Every Student's Success* at www.personalityinsights.com or www.personalityprofiles.org

Iris

IRIS is our wonderful "**I**" type personality! The letter "**I**" represents the word "**Inspiring**." "**I**" type personalities love to have fun! They are very optimistic and outgoing! They tend to be forgetful at times because they are usually in a hurry to do things! They like to move fast! Their communication style is exciting and enthusiastic. They don't do well with lots of details and information and may have difficulty accomplishing tasks because they lose their focus. They love being around other people. They thrive on attention and love to entertain others! The "**I**" type personality is **Outgoing and People-oriented**!

Summer

SUMMER is our wonderful "**S**" type personality! The letter "**S**" represents the word "**Supportive**." "**S**" type personalities are very cooperative and pleasant. They do not like conflict. They like peace and harmony. They sometimes have trouble making decisions because they tend to make up their minds slowly. Their communication style is "easy-going." In other words, they tend to adapt easily to whatever is going on around them in their environment. They love people and relationships! "**S**" types love being around other people and helping everyone they meet. They are sensitive and sometimes get their feelings hurt easily. They like to feel appreciated and secure. The "**S**" type personality is **Reserved and People-oriented**!

Charlie

CHARLIE is our wonderful "**C**" type personality! The letter "**C**" represents the word "**Cautious**." "**C**" type personalities enjoy having a routine and schedule. They are usually very good students and like things that challenge their mind. Their communication style is A to Z, which means that details and planning are very important to a "**C**." That is why they ask so many questions. The "**C**" type personality prefers to do things that have been planned out, especially if it involves a large group of people or a lot of activity. They are very comfortable being alone and working independently. They appreciate quality more than quantity. The "**C**" type personality is **Reserved and Task-oriented**!

The "**Four Pals**" series is designed to have 1 book in each series that highlights each of the four different personality styles. There will be 4 more books released in the future.

www.personalityinsights.com **or** www.personalityprofiles.org

It was a beautiful Saturday in spring. Iris had been waiting for this day for a whole week! Her mom promised to take Iris and her friends to the zoo today.

Iris loved the zoo! After all, you can run around and see all sorts of neat animals, and ride the train! How could anyone NOT love the zoo?

It was finally time for Iris' mom to pick up her friends.
Iris skipped happily, all the way to the car.

Their first stop was at David's house. David liked to go to the zoo, also. He liked to race his friends from animal to animal. He wanted to be the first person to see each one. Sometimes he even liked to race the animals to see if he could beat them from one side of their cage to the other!

7

David was waiting outside and ready to go when Iris' mom arrived. He was glad that Iris was sitting in the back seat because he liked to ride up front. He hopped in the front seat and they headed off to Summer's house.

Summer loved all of the animals at the zoo. She enjoyed watching the mother animals take care of their babies. She thought it was so cute how the mommies gave them a bath.

Summer was a very caring person herself and even brought
lunch for everyone to eat at the zoo.

Last of all, Iris' mom picked up Charlie. Charlie did not particularly like the zoo very much. He thought it was kind of a "smelly" place. But, he thought he could learn some neat things at the bug exhibit. Charlie loved to learn and always got good grades in school.

Shortly after all of Iris' friends were picked up, they arrived at the zoo. Iris immediately jumped out and tried to go inside. She forgot that you had to pay to get in! Iris could be very forgetful at times, especially when she was overly excited!

The lady working the ticket counter reminded Iris that she needed a ticket. So, she anxiously waited for her mom and friends to catch up.

Finally, everyone was inside. David took off running because he wanted to see the giraffes. He loved their long necks!

Iris asked her mom if she could have some money to buy giraffe food. She loved feeding the animals! Summer thought it was so sweet that Iris was feeding the giraffes.

Charlie, on the other hand, couldn't even imagine how someone could enjoy getting giraffe "slobber" all over their hands. He thought the giraffes had really long and ugly tongues and he certainly wasn't going to touch them!

While Iris was feeding the giraffes, she didn't notice that one of them had grabbed her entire container of food! When she found out, she laughed hysterically and asked her mom to buy more food. Her mom agreed, but said that Iris needed to keep a better eye on the giraffes!

David soon got bored and was ready to move on to the next animal. He said, "Hey, everyone, I'll race you to the monkeys!"

Everyone took off running, except for Charlie. He thought it would be better to walk so he didn't fall down and get dirty. He did not enjoy being dirty.

When they got to the monkeys, one of them was swinging upside down on a rope. Iris thought this was the funniest thing she had EVER seen and she laughed and laughed at the silly monkey.

Summer felt a little sad because the monkeys had to live in such a small area and couldn't run around as much as monkeys would like to do.

David was busy racing one monkey, although the monkey beat him every time.

Charlie thought the monkeys were very interesting creatures, but kept his distance since they might bite him.

After going to see lots of different animals and the bug exhibit, they rode the train and ate lunch. It was finally time to go.

Everyone was so tired, but they talked all the way home about what fun they had at the zoo. Even Charlie admitted that he learned some things about the animals and the bugs.

"I'm glad there were so many animals for us to see."

"Yeah, me too!" shouted David and Charlie.

"This makes me think of all the different animals there are," said Summer. "They sure are amazing!" replied David. Charlie added, "Yes, they are each very unique and different."

"I am so happy we are all such good friends!" shared Iris. "Friends are great!"

They all agreed and looked forward to their next adventure together.

Reader's Guide

This is Book 2 in this series. The focus in this book is on David – the **the Inspiring "I"** type personality! To get all four books in the "Four Pals" series go to the website: www.personalityinsights.com or www.personalityprofiles.org or call 1-800-509-DISC (3472)

David

Did you notice in this book how David was quick to be involved with all of the events of the day? He wanted to race the animals as well as lead his friends. It is okay to like to be the leader, but sometimes it is a good idea to let others go ahead of you so they can feel special, too. If you always try to get your own way you may miss out on some good ideas and plans that other people may have, especially parents and teachers. And it is a good idea to always obey the adult who is doing things with you. That way you will be more respected and have a good reputation.

The focus in this book is on Iris

Iris

Were you able to tell that Iris was full of energy and excitement? Were you also able to see how much fun Iris had by being with all of her friends? She really does enjoy being around lots and lots of people. To Iris, everyone is her best friend! She makes everyone feel like they are part of the group. Sometimes Iris forgets that following the rules helps everything go better for everyone. Her good nature helps her to always be "the life of the party". Iris is a package of fun!

Charlie

The amazing thing about Charlie is how careful he is about everything. There is just a cautious nature about him that makes him feel reserved. He simply needs a little more time to warm up to people he does not know and places he has not been before. Were you able to tell that Charlie did not simply want to look at all the animals? Charlie wants to study and learn about the animals and why each one acts the way they do. Charlie knows the zoo is a great place to learn new things! Charlie likes to be correct!

Summer

In this story could you tell how Summer loved all of the different animals? She is so kind and sincerely hopes that each of the animals is really cared for and treated nicely. Summer is always thinking of others. She believes it is important to be nice to everyone, including animals. The only part of the trip to the zoo that concerned Summer was that all the animals had enough room to move around. She didn't want any of them to feel trapped or sad. Summer tries to avoid conflict and gets along well with everyone.

"Four Pals"
and the Model of Human Behavior

Each of us has an internal "motor" that drives us. It has a fast pace that makes us more **Outgoing**, or it has a slower pace that makes us more **Reserved**. You may be extremely **Outgoing** or **Reserved**, or you may be just be moderately **Outgoing** or **Reserved**. In either case, your "internal motor" creates a certain pace about you that drives you to do your daily activities at a certain rate of speed. Knowing how you are "wired" will help you to monitor yourself in life so you will either go faster or slower depending upon the requirements or needs of the existing environment.

OUTGOING

Internal "Motor" Activity

RESERVED

Just as we have a motor that drives us, we also have a "compass" that draws us toward either task or people. Therefore, we are either **Task-oriented** or **People-oriented**. You may find yourself to be extremely **Task-oriented** or **People-oriented**, or you may be just be moderately **Task-oriented** or **People-oriented**. In either case, your "internal compass" creates a certain direction about you that drives you to do your daily activities in a certain manner that either reflects your desire to accomplish daily tasks or connect well with people. Knowing how you are "wired" will help you to monitor yourself in life so you will either focus on the task at hand or seek to relate well with the people with whom you come in contact on a daily basis, depending upon the requirements or needs of the existing environment.

TASK ← *Internal "Compass" Activity* → **PEOPLE**

When we put together both the Internal "Motor" Activity and the Internal "Compass" Activity, we see the four quadrant DIS**C** **Model of Human Behavior**. Illustrated below we see in clockwise order that:

The **D** type is
Outgoing / Task-oriented

The I type is
Outgoing / People-oriented

David
The Dominant Type

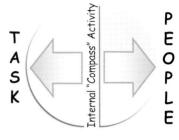

Iris
The Inspiring Type

OUTGOING & TASK   OUTGOING & PEOPLE

D I
C S

RESERVED & TASK   RESERVED & PEOPLE

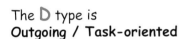
Charlie
The Cautious Type

Summer
The Supportive Type

The **C** type is
Reserved / Task-oriented

The **S** type is
Reserved / People-oriented

Introducing the Inspiring type child

Key Characteristics

| Inspiring |
| Influencing |
| Impressionable |
| Interactive |
| Impressive |
| Interested in people |

- likes to entertain others
- is impulsive
- is usually optimistic
- likes to express feelings and ideas
- is outgoing and talkative
- is very verbal and persuasive
- loves recognition and rewards
- is fun loving and playful

Value to the Family or their Group

- tries to keep people happy
- is warm, friendly, trusting
- is open with his/her feelings
- attracts people
- diffuses tension with humor
- helps people get along together
- loves to make people laugh
- brings new friends into the group

The I Danger Zone

- may speak before thinking
- lacks follow-through
- prefers talking over working
- tends to be disorganized
- is inattentive to detail
- overly optimistic, may be unrealistic

The I Type Child Says:

As a High **I** child, I love surprises! Parties and having fun things to do are what make life exciting! I like to talk about what I think and feel, so I love being with lots of people. I love to hear people say that I am doing a good job. Quick jobs are best for me, because I seem to forget details and I sometimes appear irresponsible. I like to do things when I am in the mood, so I may not like it if you just tell me what to do. I may try to talk you into letting me do things when I'm ready, or letting someone else do them. I hate it when people fight, and I try to make sure everyone has a good time. To me, a stranger is just a friend I have not yet met! Having other people like me is important, and I need to feel special and accepted by you, too. You can help me learn that it's nice to be important, but it's more important to be nice!

Keys to the heart of your Inspiring child

Communication Key – your I Child says:

- tell me who else is doing what you want me to do
- let me talk about what I am feeling
- be friendly and excited
- offer me rewards for quick jobs

Encouragement Key – say to your I Child:

- "You are fun to be with, and full of surprises!"
- "I like that you share your thoughts and feelings with me!"
- "You can make others feel so comfortable with your wonderful sense of humor."
- "When you are enthusiastic it's contagious! Let's plan to do something about that together!"

Parenting Keys for your Inspiring Child:

As you parent an I type child, you will feel like your life, and theirs, is a party! They will "light up" your life and bring sunshine into your world. They have many friends and love to be doing something with them all the time. Making things fun for everyone who is important gives them the recognition and approval from their friends they need. This is a strong need for the I child. However, the emotions they feel with this need may get them into trouble. They want to be liked so much that they will try to impress others. This can lead to making bad choices in the heat of the moment. They need a foundation of your loving recognition and approval to strengthen them to help them make wise choices in life. Enjoying lots of fun activities together with you will strengthen this bond.

The I child is an enthusiastic starter and can focus on short term assignments. In other words, they are a better starter than finisher! They tend to be totally involved at the beginning of a project because it is new and exciting. However, they quickly lose interest when the "new" has worn off. Learning to run a marathon is very different than running a sprint. You will want to teach them how to think and work on a long term basis. Their motto might be, "Inch by inch everything is a cinch, but by the yard everything is hard." If they can learn how to better pace themselves and stick with projects until completion, there is no end to their success! This child is a real prize!

About the Authors

Angel Tucker is a wife, mom and national speaker/trainer. As a Certified Human Behavior Consultant and owner of Personality Profiles, LLC, she has been speaking and training professionally across North America for the past 23 years. She began by teaching churches and youth groups. She instantly knew it was her desire to share this life changing information with as many people as possible. Angel and her husband Dennis, who is an officer in the United States Air Force, have five children – Danielle, Chase, Hannah, Elijah and Ava. When Dennis retires, they plan to travel the country together – teaching and training others about our wonderful personalities!

If you are interested in having Angel speak at your next engagement, please contact her using the following information:

Website: www.personalityprofiles.org
Email: personalitypro@msn.com

Dr. Robert A. Rohm is a renowned National and International speaker. He has traveled all over the world including every continent (except Antarctica), teaching and training people in the D-I-S-C Model of Human Behavior. Most people consider Dr. Rohm to be one of the leading authorities in the world on understanding personality styles and relationship dynamics.

Dr. Rohm has been an educator for over 40 years. He has earned 5 college degrees and has written or co-authored over 20 books as well as writing over 600 published articles. He also has numerous audio and video training programs including two PBS Specials.

Dr. Rohm is a husband, father and grandfather and believes that those roles have been the true source for many of his insights and learning experiences. He has entertained and enlightened audiences for many years. His mixture of stories, illustrations, and humor make him a gifted speaker to audiences of all ages!

Dr. Rohm is also the co-founder of discoveryreport.com

To learn more about Dr. Robert Rohm or have him at your event, go to: www.robertrohm.com or www.personalityinsights.com or call Personality Insights, Inc. at (800) 509-DISC (3472).

Discover more...

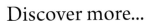

Here is one of the most accurate tools available for DISCovering children's personality styles. Purpose: To help parents, teachers and individuals who work with children better understand them, and for the children to understand themselves and others by explaining tendencies. This resource material provides insights on tendencies as your child develops and matures. Additional insights are approaching instructions, motivational tips, and pointers on ideal environment and communication.

On-line Assessment and Personalized Report

Children's Version   *(Ages 5 -12)*

This one-of-a-kind assessment is designed specifically for children. It is a fun and interactive way for parents and teachers to gain insights into individual preferences or choices the child makes based on robot characters (BOTS).

The stories allow children as young as 5 years old to complete the assessment.

www.personalityinsights.com

www.personalityprofiles.org

www.discoveryreport.com